POWER TO
DREAM
Again

"UNLOCKING THE MYSTERIES OF
DREAMS & VISIONS"

JOURNAL

MATTIE
NOTTAGE

THE POWER TO DREAM AGAIN
The Journal

Published By:
Mattie Nottage Ministries, International
P.O. Box SB–52524
Nassau, N. P. Bahamas
Tel: (888) 825-7568 or (242) 698-1383
www.mattienottage.org

Unless otherwise indicated, all Scripture quotations are taken from the King James Version, biblegateway.com and The Amplified Bible ©1987 by the Zondervan Corporation and the Lockman Foundation, Grand Rapids, Michigan.

Cover design by: Beyond All Barriers Publications & Media Group
Edited by: Beyond All Barriers Publications & Media Group
Format and Interior design by:
Beyond All Barriers Publications & Media Group
Copyright ©2020 by Mattie M. Nottage
All rights reserved.

Printed in the United States of America
First Printing: February 2020
ISBN: 978-1-951110—04-8

THE POWER TO DREAM AGAIN
The Journal

———◄I◆I►———

This companion journal to *"The Power To Dream Again!"* book is a personal tool which allows you to freely document every dream, vision, trance or impression that you experience during the night watches or even during the day.

This journal will allow you to not only write down the dream that God is showing you, but will also allow you to make note of relevant scriptures, images, colors, animals and the like as you continue to navigate the prophetic pathways to interpreting the meaning of your dreams.

I pray that you will be able to discern when your dream is from God and when it is from the devil. Further, I pray that you will become spiritually mature enough to embrace your godly dreams and spiritually militant to go to battle against every bad dream, nightmares, or demonic enemy seeking to enter your life through your dream realm.

Meditate upon your dreams through the Word of God and spend much time in prayer and worship before Him. Allow Him to minister the truth of what He is speaking and saying to you through your dreams.

It is the glory of God to conceal a thing: but the honour of kings is to search out a matter.
(Proverbs 25:2)

In **Proverbs 25:2**, the Word of God speaks volumes as it admonishes us that it is an honor to be able to interpret the counsel of God that He has released through a dream, vision or even a parable. It is given to the people of God to know the mysteries and profound kingdom truths that He has encoded throughout the annuls of time and even in our dispensation.

Such unveiling of mysteries has revealed economic breakthroughs, prophetic insight, the end of demonic world governments, modern day discoveries and inventions; they have unlocked divine destinies, unsurpassed wisdom and insight, divine purpose, godly relationships, deceitful enemies and so much more.

Our God is an awesome God and worthy of all praise and glory. He is the God of all wisdom, knowledge and understanding. He has established the foundation of the world and everything in it. It is His desire that we seek to know Him; that we pursue hard after Him as He teaches us His ways, His precepts and counsel. It is truly an honor to know our God; to be able to hear and perceive Him through the mysteries with which He speaks to us.

I encourage you to embrace the dream realm with godly wisdom, counsel and understanding as you seek to uncover the mysteries and hidden messages in your dreams as God gives them to you! I pray that on this journey that you truly find the power and courage to dream again!!.....***God bless you!***

With Love,
Dr. Mattie Nottage

God Speaks Through Dreams & Visions

14

**For God speaks once, yea twice,
yet man perceiveth it not.**

15

**In a dream, in a vision of the night,
when deep sleep falleth upon men,
in slumberings upon the bed;
(Job 33:14, 15)**

Welcome to your Personal Dream Journal....

Date: _____ Time: _____

Scriptures: _____

_____

_____

_____

Significant Signs/Symbols:

_____

_____

_____

_____

_____

My Dream Was About:

_____

_____

_____

_____

_____

_____

_____

_____

_____

THE POWER TO DREAM AGAIN!

"Unlocking The Mysteries of Dreams & Visions!"

_____

_____

_____

_____

_____

_____

_____

_____

_____

_____

_____

_____

_____

_____

_____

_____

_____

_____

_____

_____

_____

_____

And it shall come to pass afterward, that I will pour out my spirit upon all flesh; and your sons and your daughters shall prophesy, your old men shall dream dreams, your young men shall see visions: **Joel 2:28**

"Unlocking The Mysteries of Dreams & Visions!"

_____

_____

_____

_____

_____

_____

_____

_____

_____

_____

_____

_____

_____

_____

_____

_____

_____

_____

_____

_____

_____

_____

_____

_____

_____

_____

"Unlocking The Mysteries of Dreams & Visions!"

_____

_____

_____

_____

_____

_____

_____

_____

_____

_____

_____

_____

_____

_____

_____

_____

_____

_____

_____

_____

_____

_____

_____

"Unlocking The Mysteries of Dreams & Visions!"

_____

_____

_____

_____

_____

_____

_____

_____

_____

_____

_____

_____

_____

_____

_____

_____

_____

_____

_____

_____

_____

_____

_____

_____

_____

_____

_____

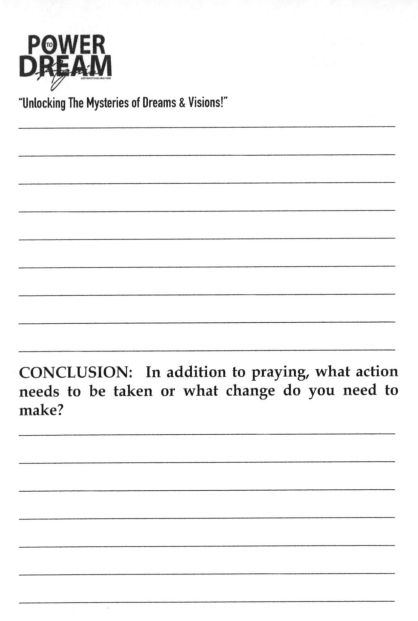

POWER TO **DREAM**

"Unlocking The Mysteries of Dreams & Visions!"

_____

_____

_____

_____

_____

_____

_____

_____

_____

CONCLUSION: In addition to praying, what action needs to be taken or what change do you need to make?

_____

_____

_____

_____

_____

_____

_____

_____

_____

_____

_____

_____

THE POWER TO DREAM AGAIN!

"Unlocking The Mysteries of Dreams & Visions!"

Date: _____ Time: _____

Scriptures: _____

_____

_____

_____

Significant Signs/Symbols:

_____

_____

_____

_____

_____

My Dream Was About:

_____

_____

_____

_____

_____

_____

_____

_____

_____

THE POWER TO DREAM AGAIN!

POWER TO DREAM

"Unlocking The Mysteries of Dreams & Visions!"

_____

_____

_____

_____

_____

_____

_____

_____

_____

_____

_____

_____

_____

_____

_____

_____

_____

_____

_____

_____

_____

_____

_____

_____

_____

_____

But without faith it is impossible to please him: for he that cometh to God must believe that he is, and that he is a rewarder of them that diligently seek him. **Hebrews 11:6**

"Unlocking The Mysteries of Dreams & Visions!"

_____

_____

_____

_____

_____

_____

_____

_____

_____

_____

_____

_____

_____

_____

_____

_____

_____

_____

_____

_____

_____

_____

_____

"Unlocking The Mysteries of Dreams & Visions!"

_____

_____

_____

_____

_____

_____

_____

_____

_____

_____

_____

_____

_____

_____

_____

_____

_____

_____

_____

_____

_____

_____

_____

_____

_____

_____

_____

"Unlocking The Mysteries of Dreams & Visions!"

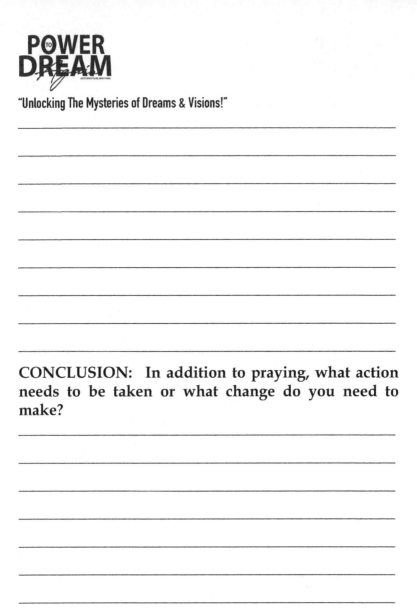

_____

_____

_____

_____

_____

_____

_____

_____

CONCLUSION: In addition to praying, what action needs to be taken or what change do you need to make?

_____

_____

_____

_____

_____

_____

_____

_____

_____

_____

_____

THE POWER TO DREAM AGAIN!

"Unlocking The Mysteries of Dreams & Visions!"

Date: _____ Time: _____

Scriptures: _____

_____

_____

_____

Significant Signs/Symbols:

_____

_____

_____

_____

My Dream Was About:

_____

_____

_____

_____

_____

_____

_____

_____

_____

_____

THE POWER TO DREAM AGAIN!

POWER TO DREAM

"Unlocking The Mysteries of Dreams & Visions!"

_____

_____

_____

_____

_____

_____

_____

_____

_____

_____

_____

_____

_____

_____

_____

_____

_____

_____

_____

_____

_____

_____

_____

_____

But the natural man receiveth not the things of the Spirit of God:
for they are foolishness unto him: neither can he know them,
because they are spiritually discerned. **1 Corinthians 2:14**

"Unlocking The Mysteries of Dreams & Visions!"

_____

_____

_____

_____

_____

_____

_____

_____

_____

_____

_____

_____

_____

_____

_____

_____

_____

_____

_____

_____

_____

_____

_____

_____

_____

_____

_____

"Unlocking The Mysteries of Dreams & Visions!"

"Unlocking The Mysteries of Dreams & Visions!"

_____

_____

_____

_____

_____

_____

_____

_____

_____

_____

_____

_____

_____

_____

_____

_____

_____

_____

_____

_____

_____

_____

_____

_____

_____

_____

_____

_____

_____

_____

_____

_____

_____

_____

_____

_____

_____

CONCLUSION: In addition to praying, what action needs to be taken or what change do you need to make?

_____

_____

_____

_____

_____

_____

_____

_____

_____

_____

THE POWER TO DREAM AGAIN!

POWER TO **DREAM**

"Unlocking The Mysteries of Dreams & Visions!"

Date: _____ Time: _____

Scriptures: _____

_____

_____

_____

Significant Signs/Symbols:

_____

_____

_____

_____

My Dream Was About:

_____

_____

_____

_____

_____

_____

_____

_____

_____

THE POWER TO DREAM AGAIN!

"Unlocking The Mysteries of Dreams & Visions!"

_____

_____

_____

_____

_____

_____

_____

_____

_____

_____

_____

_____

_____

_____

_____

_____

_____

_____

_____

_____

_____

_____

_____

For the prophecy came not in old time by the will of man: but holy men of
God spake as they were moved by the Holy Ghost. **2 Peter 1:21**

"Unlocking The Mysteries of Dreams & Visions!"

_____

_____

_____

_____

_____

_____

_____

_____

_____

_____

_____

_____

_____

_____

_____

_____

_____

_____

_____

_____

_____

_____

_____

_____

_____

_____

_____

POWER TO DREAM

"Unlocking The Mysteries of Dreams & Visions!"

_____
_____
_____
_____
_____
_____
_____
_____
_____
_____
_____
_____
_____
_____
_____
_____
_____
_____
_____
_____
_____
_____
_____
_____
_____
_____

"Unlocking The Mysteries of Dreams & Visions!"

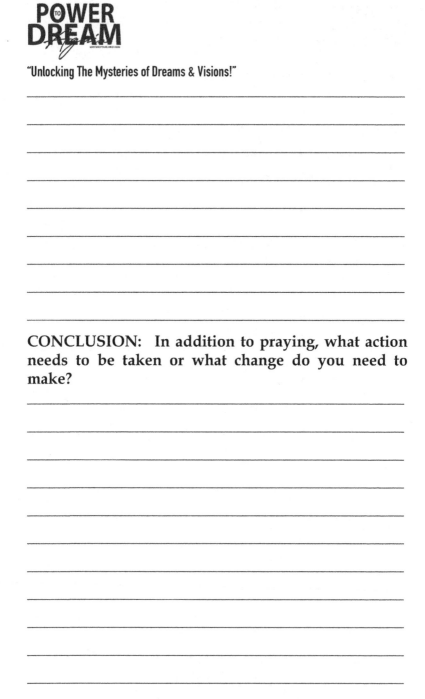

_____

_____

_____

_____

_____

_____

_____

_____

_____

CONCLUSION: In addition to praying, what action needs to be taken or what change do you need to make?

_____

_____

_____

_____

_____

_____

_____

_____

_____

_____

_____

THE POWER TO DREAM AGAIN!

POWER TO **DREAM**

"Unlocking The Mysteries of Dreams & Visions!"

Date: _____ **Time:** _____

Scriptures: _____

_____

_____

_____

Significant Signs/Symbols:

_____

_____

_____

_____

_____

My Dream Was About:

_____

_____

_____

_____

_____

_____

_____

_____

_____

THE POWER TO DREAM AGAIN!

"Unlocking The Mysteries of Dreams & Visions!"

Wisdom is the principal thing; therefore get wisdom: and with all thy
getting get understanding. **Proverbs 4:7**

"Unlocking The Mysteries of Dreams & Visions!"

"Unlocking The Mysteries of Dreams & Visions!"

_____

_____

_____

_____

_____

_____

_____

_____

_____

_____

_____

_____

_____

_____

_____

_____

_____

_____

_____

_____

_____

_____

_____

_____

"Unlocking The Mysteries of Dreams & Visions!"

_____

_____

_____

_____

_____

_____

_____

_____

_____

_____

_____

_____

_____

_____

_____

_____

_____

_____

_____

_____

_____

_____

_____

_____

_____

_____

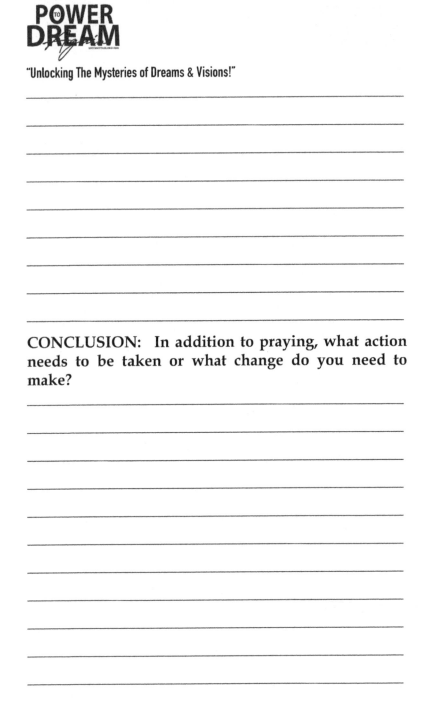

_____

_____

_____

_____

_____

_____

_____

_____

CONCLUSION: In addition to praying, what action needs to be taken or what change do you need to make?

_____

_____

_____

_____

_____

_____

_____

_____

_____

_____

THE POWER TO DREAM AGAIN!

"Unlocking The Mysteries of Dreams & Visions!"

Date: _____ Time: _____

Scriptures: _____

_____

_____

_____

Significant Signs/Symbols:

_____

_____

_____

_____

_____

My Dream Was About:

_____

_____

_____

_____

_____

_____

_____

_____

_____

THE POWER TO DREAM AGAIN!

"Unlocking The Mysteries of Dreams & Visions!"

_____

_____

_____

_____

_____

_____

_____

_____

_____

_____

_____

_____

_____

_____

_____

_____

_____

_____

_____

_____

_____

_____

_____

I have also spoken by the prophets, and I have multiplied visions, and used similitudes, by the ministry of the prophets. **Hosea 12:10**

"Unlocking The Mysteries of Dreams & Visions!"

_____

_____

_____

_____

_____

_____

_____

_____

_____

_____

_____

_____

_____

_____

_____

_____

_____

_____

_____

_____

_____

_____

_____

"Unlocking The Mysteries of Dreams & Visions!"

_____

_____

_____

_____

_____

_____

_____

_____

_____

_____

_____

_____

_____

_____

_____

_____

_____

_____

_____

_____

_____

_____

_____

_____

_____

_____

_____

_____

"Unlocking The Mysteries of Dreams & Visions!"

_____

_____

_____

_____

_____

_____

_____

_____

_____

_____

_____

_____

_____

_____

_____

_____

_____

_____

_____

_____

_____

_____

_____

_____

_____

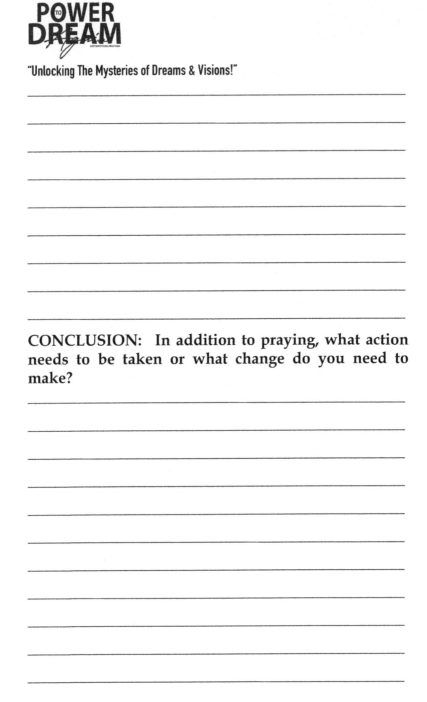

_____

_____

_____

_____

_____

_____

_____

_____

_____

CONCLUSION: In addition to praying, what action needs to be taken or what change do you need to make?

_____

_____

_____

_____

_____

_____

_____

_____

_____

_____

_____

THE POWER TO DREAM AGAIN!

"Unlocking The Mysteries of Dreams & Visions!"

Date: _____ Time: _____

Scriptures: _____

_____

_____

_____

Significant Signs/Symbols:

_____

_____

_____

_____

_____

My Dream Was About:

_____

_____

_____

_____

_____

_____

_____

_____

_____

THE POWER TO DREAM AGAIN!

"Unlocking The Mysteries of Dreams & Visions!"

_____

_____

_____

_____

_____

_____

_____

_____

_____

_____

_____

_____

_____

_____

_____

_____

_____

_____

_____

_____

_____

_____

_____

_____

_____

For I know the thoughts that I think toward you, saith the Lord,
thoughts of peace, and not of evil, to give you an expected end.
Jeremiah 29:11

"Unlocking The Mysteries of Dreams & Visions!"

_____

_____

_____

_____

_____

_____

_____

_____

_____

_____

_____

_____

_____

_____

_____

_____

_____

_____

_____

_____

_____

_____

_____

"Unlocking The Mysteries of Dreams & Visions!"

_____

_____

_____

_____

_____

_____

_____

_____

_____

_____

_____

_____

_____

_____

_____

_____

_____

_____

_____

_____

_____

_____

_____

_____

_____

"Unlocking The Mysteries of Dreams & Visions!"

_____

_____

_____

_____

_____

_____

_____

_____

_____

_____

_____

_____

_____

_____

_____

_____

_____

_____

_____

_____

_____

_____

_____

_____

_____

_____

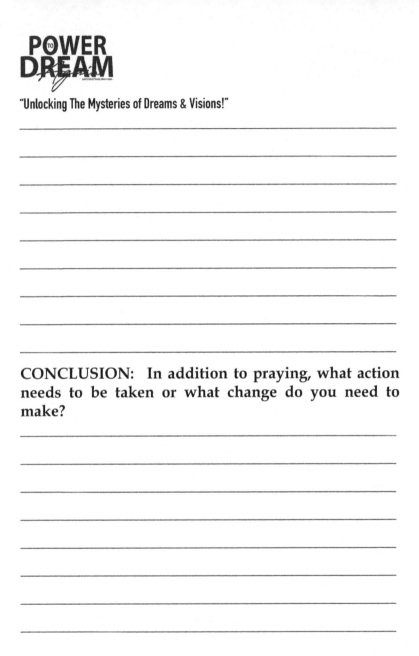

"Unlocking The Mysteries of Dreams & Visions!"

_____

_____

_____

_____

_____

_____

_____

_____

_____

CONCLUSION: In addition to praying, what action needs to be taken or what change do you need to make?

_____

_____

_____

_____

_____

_____

_____

_____

_____

_____

_____

THE POWER TO DREAM AGAIN!

"Unlocking The Mysteries of Dreams & Visions!"

Date: _____ Time: _____

Scriptures: _____

_____

_____

_____

Significant Signs/Symbols:

_____

_____

_____

_____

_____

My Dream Was About:

_____

_____

_____

_____

_____

_____

_____

_____

_____

_____

THE POWER TO DREAM AGAIN!

"Unlocking The Mysteries of Dreams & Visions!"

_____

_____

_____

_____

_____

_____

_____

_____

_____

_____

_____

_____

_____

_____

_____

_____

_____

_____

_____

_____

_____

_____

_____

Surely the Lord God will do nothing, but he revealeth his secret unto his
servants the prophets. **Amos 3:7**

"Unlocking The Mysteries of Dreams & Visions!"

_____

_____

_____

_____

_____

_____

_____

_____

_____

_____

_____

_____

_____

_____

_____

_____

_____

_____

_____

_____

_____

_____

_____

"Unlocking The Mysteries of Dreams & Visions!"

_____

_____

_____

_____

_____

_____

_____

_____

_____

_____

_____

_____

_____

_____

_____

_____

_____

_____

_____

_____

_____

_____

_____

_____

_____

_____

_____

_____

"Unlocking The Mysteries of Dreams & Visions!"

_____

_____

_____

_____

_____

_____

_____

_____

_____

_____

_____

_____

_____

_____

_____

_____

_____

_____

_____

_____

_____

_____

_____

_____

_____

_____

_____

_____

_____

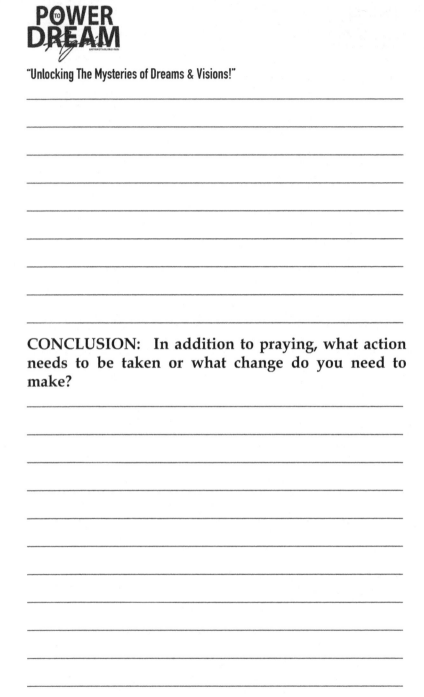

_____

_____

_____

_____

_____

_____

_____

CONCLUSION: In addition to praying, what action needs to be taken or what change do you need to make?

_____

_____

_____

_____

_____

_____

_____

_____

_____

_____

THE POWER TO DREAM AGAIN!

"Unlocking The Mysteries of Dreams & Visions!"

Date: _____ Time: _____

Scriptures: _____

_____

_____

_____

Significant Signs/Symbols:

_____

_____

_____

_____

_____

My Dream Was About:

_____

_____

_____

_____

_____

_____

_____

_____

_____

_____

THE POWER TO DREAM AGAIN!

"Unlocking The Mysteries of Dreams & Visions!"

_____

_____

_____

_____

_____

_____

_____

_____

_____

_____

_____

_____

_____

_____

_____

_____

_____

_____

_____

_____

_____

_____

_____

_____

Call unto me, and I will answer thee, and show thee great
and mighty things, which thou knowest not. **Jeremiah 33:3**

"Unlocking The Mysteries of Dreams & Visions!"

_____

_____

_____

_____

_____

_____

_____

_____

_____

_____

_____

_____

_____

_____

_____

_____

_____

_____

_____

_____

_____

_____

_____

_____

"Unlocking The Mysteries of Dreams & Visions!"

_____

_____

_____

_____

_____

_____

_____

_____

_____

_____

_____

_____

_____

_____

_____

_____

_____

_____

_____

_____

_____

_____

_____

"Unlocking The Mysteries of Dreams & Visions!"

_____

_____

_____

_____

_____

_____

_____

_____

_____

_____

_____

_____

_____

_____

_____

_____

_____

_____

_____

_____

_____

_____

_____

_____

_____

_____

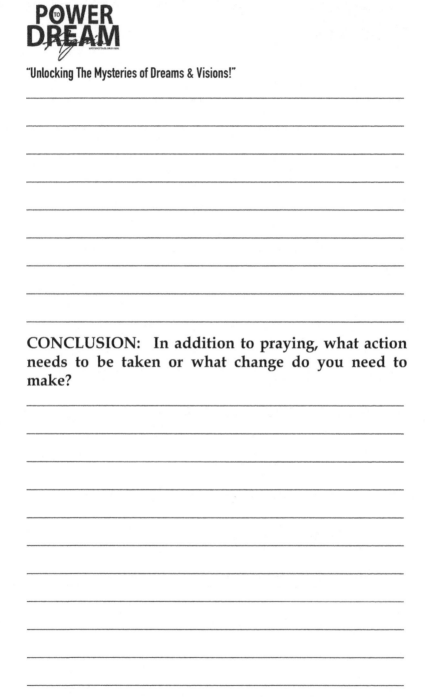

POWER TO DREAM

"Unlocking The Mysteries of Dreams & Visions!"

_____

_____

_____

_____

_____

_____

_____

_____

_____

CONCLUSION: In addition to praying, what action needs to be taken or what change do you need to make?

_____

_____

_____

_____

_____

_____

_____

_____

_____

_____

THE POWER TO DREAM AGAIN!

"Unlocking The Mysteries of Dreams & Visions!"

_____

Date: _____ Time: _____

Scriptures: _____

_____

_____

_____

Significant Signs/Symbols:

_____

_____

_____

_____

_____

My Dream Was About:

_____

_____

_____

_____

_____

_____

_____

_____

_____

_____

THE POWER TO DREAM AGAIN!

"Unlocking The Mysteries of Dreams & Visions!"

_____

_____

_____

_____

_____

_____

_____

_____

_____

_____

_____

_____

_____

_____

_____

_____

_____

_____

_____

_____

_____

_____

_____

_____

And Elisha prayed, and said, Lord, I pray thee, open his eyes, that he may see. And the Lord opened the eyes of the young man;... **2 Kings 6:17a**

"Unlocking The Mysteries of Dreams & Visions!"

_____

_____

_____

_____

_____

_____

_____

_____

_____

_____

_____

_____

_____

_____

_____

_____

_____

_____

_____

_____

_____

_____

_____

"Unlocking The Mysteries of Dreams & Visions!"

"Unlocking The Mysteries of Dreams & Visions!"

_____

_____

_____

_____

_____

_____

_____

_____

CONCLUSION: In addition to praying, what action needs to be taken or what change do you need to make?

_____

_____

_____

_____

_____

_____

_____

_____

_____

THE POWER TO DREAM AGAIN!

POWER
DREAM

"Unlocking The Mysteries of Dreams & Visions!"

_____

Date: _____ Time: _____

Scriptures: _____

_____

_____

_____

Significant Signs/Symbols:

_____

_____

_____

_____

My Dream Was About:

_____

_____

_____

_____

_____

_____

_____

_____

_____

THE POWER TO DREAM AGAIN!

"Unlocking The Mysteries of Dreams & Visions!"

_____

_____

_____

_____

_____

_____

_____

_____

_____

_____

_____

_____

_____

_____

_____

_____

_____

_____

_____

_____

_____

_____

_____

_____

He hath said, which heard the words of God, which saw the vision of the Almighty, falling into a trance, but having his eyes open: **Numbers 24:4**

"Unlocking The Mysteries of Dreams & Visions!"

_____

_____

_____

_____

_____

_____

_____

_____

_____

_____

_____

_____

_____

_____

_____

_____

_____

_____

_____

_____

_____

_____

_____

_____

_____

"Unlocking The Mysteries of Dreams & Visions!"

_____

_____

_____

_____

_____

_____

_____

_____

_____

_____

_____

_____

_____

_____

_____

_____

_____

_____

_____

_____

_____

_____

_____

_____

_____

_____

_____

"Unlocking The Mysteries of Dreams & Visions!"

_____

_____

_____

_____

_____

_____

_____

_____

_____

_____

_____

_____

_____

_____

_____

_____

_____

_____

_____

_____

_____

_____

_____

_____

_____

_____

_____

_____

_____

_____

_____

_____

_____

_____

_____

_____

_____

_____

CONCLUSION: In addition to praying, what action needs to be taken or what change do you need to make?

_____

_____

_____

_____

_____

_____

_____

_____

_____

_____

_____

_____

_____

THE POWER TO DREAM AGAIN!

"Unlocking The Mysteries of Dreams & Visions!"

Date: _____ Time: _____

Scriptures: _____

_____

_____

_____

Significant Signs/Symbols:

_____

_____

_____

_____

_____

My Dream Was About:

_____

_____

_____

_____

_____

_____

_____

_____

_____

THE POWER TO DREAM AGAIN!

"Unlocking The Mysteries of Dreams & Visions!"

_____

_____

_____

_____

_____

_____

_____

_____

_____

_____

_____

_____

_____

_____

_____

_____

_____

_____

_____

_____

_____

_____

_____

To open their eyes, and to turn them from darkness to light, and from the
power of satan unto God,... **Acts 26:18**

"Unlocking The Mysteries of Dreams & Visions!"

_____

_____

_____

_____

_____

_____

_____

_____

_____

_____

_____

_____

_____

_____

_____

_____

_____

_____

_____

_____

_____

_____

_____

_____

_____

_____

"Unlocking The Mysteries of Dreams & Visions!"

_____

_____

_____

_____

_____

_____

_____

_____

_____

_____

_____

_____

_____

_____

_____

_____

_____

_____

_____

_____

_____

_____

_____

"Unlocking The Mysteries of Dreams & Visions!"

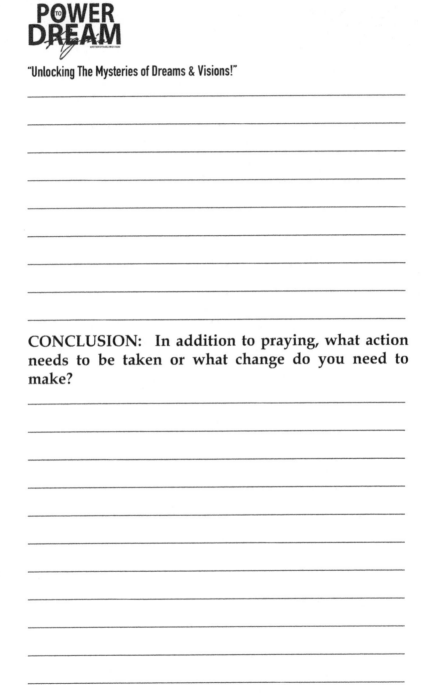

_____

_____

_____

_____

_____

_____

_____

_____

CONCLUSION: In addition to praying, what action needs to be taken or what change do you need to make?

_____

_____

_____

_____

_____

_____

_____

_____

_____

_____

THE POWER TO DREAM AGAIN!

"Unlocking The Mysteries of Dreams & Visions!"

Date: _____ Time: _____

Scriptures: _____

_____

_____

_____

Significant Signs/Symbols:

_____

_____

_____

_____

_____

My Dream Was About:

_____

_____

_____

_____

_____

_____

_____

_____

_____

_____

THE POWER TO DREAM AGAIN!

POWER DREAM

"Unlocking The Mysteries of Dreams & Visions!"

_____

_____

_____

_____

_____

_____

_____

_____

_____

_____

_____

_____

_____

_____

_____

_____

_____

_____

_____

_____

_____

_____

_____

Howbeit when he, the Spirit of truth, is come, he will guide you into all truth:...and he will shew you things to come. **John 16:13**

"Unlocking The Mysteries of Dreams & Visions!"

_____

_____

_____

_____

_____

_____

_____

_____

_____

_____

_____

_____

_____

_____

_____

_____

_____

_____

_____

_____

_____

_____

_____

"Unlocking The Mysteries of Dreams & Visions!"

_____

_____

_____

_____

_____

_____

_____

_____

_____

_____

_____

_____

_____

_____

_____

_____

_____

_____

_____

_____

_____

_____

_____

_____

_____

"Unlocking The Mysteries of Dreams & Visions!"

POWER ᵀᴼ DREAM

"Unlocking The Mysteries of Dreams & Visions!"

_____

_____

_____

_____

_____

_____

_____

_____

CONCLUSION: In addition to praying, what action needs
to be taken or what change do you need to make?

_____

_____

_____

_____

_____

_____

_____

_____

_____

_____

THE POWER TO DREAM AGAIN!

"Unlocking The Mysteries of Dreams & Visions!"

Date: _____ Time: _____

Scriptures: _____

_____

_____

_____

Significant Signs/Symbols:

_____

_____

_____

_____

_____

My Dream Was About:

_____

_____

_____

_____

_____

_____

_____

_____

_____

THE POWER TO DREAM AGAIN!

"Unlocking The Mysteries of Dreams & Visions!"

_____

_____

_____

_____

_____

_____

_____

_____

_____

_____

_____

_____

_____

_____

_____

_____

_____

_____

_____

_____

_____

_____

_____

_____

_____

_____

Jesus answered and said unto him, Verily, verily, I say unto thee,
Except a man be born again, he cannot see the kingdom of God.
John 3:3

"Unlocking The Mysteries of Dreams & Visions!"

_____

_____

_____

_____

_____

_____

_____

_____

_____

_____

_____

_____

_____

_____

_____

_____

_____

_____

_____

_____

_____

_____

_____

_____

_____

"Unlocking The Mysteries of Dreams & Visions!"

_____

_____

_____

_____

_____

_____

_____

_____

_____

_____

_____

_____

_____

_____

_____

_____

_____

_____

_____

_____

_____

_____

_____

_____

_____

_____

_____

"Unlocking The Mysteries of Dreams & Visions!"

_____

_____

_____

_____

_____

_____

_____

_____

_____

_____

_____

_____

_____

_____

_____

_____

_____

_____

_____

_____

_____

_____

_____

_____

_____

_____

_____

_____

_____

_____

_____

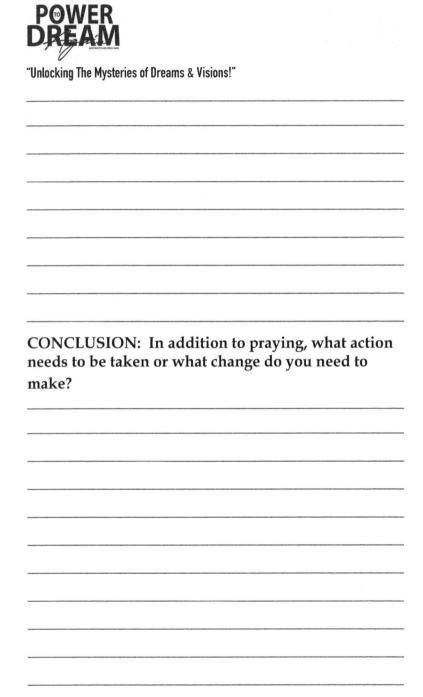

_____

_____

_____

_____

_____

_____

_____

_____

CONCLUSION: In addition to praying, what action needs to be taken or what change do you need to make?

_____

_____

_____

_____

_____

_____

_____

_____

_____

_____

_____

THE POWER TO DREAM AGAIN!

POWER TO DREAM

"Unlocking The Mysteries of Dreams & Visions!"

Date: _____ Time: _____

Scriptures: _____

_____

_____

_____

Significant Signs/Symbols:

_____

_____

_____

_____

_____

My Dream Was About:

_____

_____

_____

_____

_____

_____

_____

_____

_____

THE POWER TO DREAM AGAIN!

"Unlocking The Mysteries of Dreams & Visions!"

_____

_____

_____

_____

_____

_____

_____

_____

_____

_____

_____

_____

_____

_____

_____

_____

_____

_____

_____

_____

_____

_____

_____

_____

In Gibeon the Lord appeared to Solomon in a dream by night: and God
said, Ask what I shall give thee. **1 Kings 3:5**

"Unlocking The Mysteries of Dreams & Visions!"

_____

_____

_____

_____

_____

_____

_____

_____

_____

_____

_____

_____

_____

_____

_____

_____

_____

_____

_____

_____

_____

_____

_____

"Unlocking The Mysteries of Dreams & Visions!"

"Unlocking The Mysteries of Dreams & Visions!"

_____

_____

_____

_____

_____

_____

_____

_____

_____

_____

_____

_____

_____

_____

_____

_____

_____

_____

_____

_____

_____

_____

_____

_____

_____

_____

_____

_____

_____

_____

_____

_____

_____

_____

_____

_____

_____

CONCLUSION: In addition to praying, what action needs to be taken or what change do you need to make?

_____

_____

_____

_____

_____

_____

_____

_____

_____

_____

_____

THE POWER TO DREAM AGAIN!

"Unlocking The Mysteries of Dreams & Visions!"

Date: _____ **Time:** _____

Scriptures: _____

_____

_____

_____

Significant Signs/Symbols:

_____

_____

_____

_____

_____

My Dream Was About:

_____

_____

_____

_____

_____

_____

_____

_____

_____

THE POWER TO DREAM AGAIN!

"Unlocking The Mysteries of Dreams & Visions!"

_____

_____

_____

_____

_____

_____

_____

_____

_____

_____

_____

_____

_____

_____

_____

_____

_____

_____

_____

_____

_____

_____

_____

_____

Where there is no vision, the people perish: but he that keepeth the law,
happy is he. **Proverbs 29:18**

"Unlocking The Mysteries of Dreams & Visions!"

POWER TO DREAM

"Unlocking The Mysteries of Dreams & Visions!"

_____

_____

_____

_____

_____

_____

_____

_____

_____

_____

_____

_____

_____

_____

_____

_____

_____

_____

_____

_____

_____

_____

_____

_____

_____

_____

"Unlocking The Mysteries of Dreams & Visions!"

_____

_____

_____

_____

_____

_____

_____

_____

_____

_____

_____

_____

_____

_____

_____

_____

_____

_____

_____

_____

_____

_____

_____

_____

_____

_____

_____

_____

_____

_____

_____

_____

_____

_____

_____

_____

_____

_____

CONCLUSION: In addition to praying, what action needs to be taken or what change do you need to make?

_____

_____

_____

_____

_____

_____

_____

_____

_____

_____

_____

THE POWER TO DREAM AGAIN!

"Unlocking The Mysteries of Dreams & Visions!"

_____

Date: _____ Time: _____

Scriptures: _____

_____

_____

_____

Significant Signs/Symbols:

_____

_____

_____

_____

_____

My Dream Was About:

_____

_____

_____

_____

_____

_____

_____

_____

_____

THE POWER TO DREAM AGAIN!

"Unlocking The Mysteries of Dreams & Visions!"

_____

_____

_____

_____

_____

_____

_____

_____

_____

_____

_____

_____

_____

_____

_____

_____

_____

_____

_____

_____

_____

_____

_____

_____

_____

And the Lord answered me, and said, Write the vision, and make it
plain upon tables, that he may run that readeth it. **Habakkuk 2:2**

"Unlocking The Mysteries of Dreams & Visions!"

_____

_____

_____

_____

_____

_____

_____

_____

_____

_____

_____

_____

_____

_____

_____

_____

_____

_____

_____

_____

_____

_____

_____

_____

_____

"Unlocking The Mysteries of Dreams & Visions!"

"Unlocking The Mysteries of Dreams & Visions!"

_____

_____

_____

_____

_____

_____

_____

_____

CONCLUSION: In addition to praying, what action needs to be taken or what change do you need to make?

_____

_____

_____

_____

_____

_____

_____

_____

_____

_____

_____

THE POWER TO DREAM AGAIN!

"Unlocking The Mysteries of Dreams & Visions!"

Date: _____ Time: _____

Scriptures: _____

_____

_____

_____

Significant Signs/Symbols:

_____

_____

_____

_____

_____

My Dream Was About:

_____

_____

_____

_____

_____

_____

_____

_____

_____

THE POWER TO DREAM AGAIN!

"Unlocking The Mysteries of Dreams & Visions!"

_____

_____

_____

_____

_____

_____

_____

_____

_____

_____

_____

_____

_____

_____

_____

_____

_____

_____

_____

_____

_____

_____

_____

_____

_____

_____

_____

For the vision is yet for an appointed time, but at the end it shall
speak, and not lie: though it tarry, wait for it; because it will surely
come, it will not tarry. **Habakkuk 2:3**

"Unlocking The Mysteries of Dreams & Visions!"

_____

_____

_____

_____

_____

_____

_____

_____

_____

_____

_____

_____

_____

_____

_____

_____

_____

_____

_____

_____

_____

_____

_____

_____

_____

_____

"Unlocking The Mysteries of Dreams & Visions!"

_____

_____

_____

_____

_____

_____

_____

_____

_____

_____

_____

_____

_____

_____

_____

_____

_____

_____

_____

_____

_____

_____

_____

_____

_____

_____

"Unlocking The Mysteries of Dreams & Visions!"

_____

_____

_____

_____

_____

_____

_____

_____

_____

_____

_____

_____

_____

_____

_____

_____

_____

_____

_____

_____

_____

_____

_____

_____

_____

_____

_____

_____

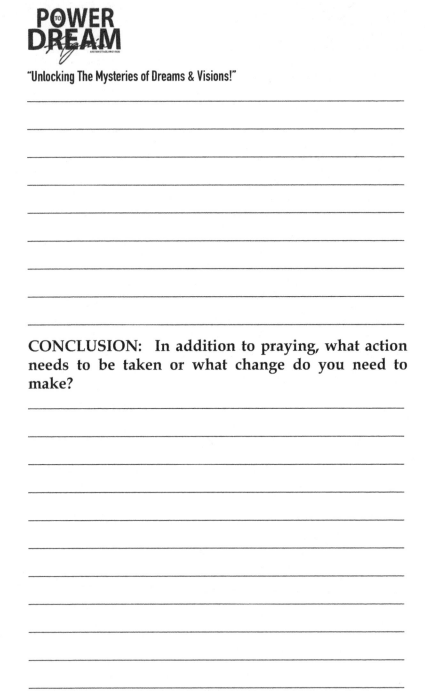

POWER
DREAM

"Unlocking The Mysteries of Dreams & Visions!"

_____

_____

_____

_____

_____

_____

_____

_____

CONCLUSION: In addition to praying, what action needs to be taken or what change do you need to make?

_____

_____

_____

_____

_____

_____

_____

_____

_____

_____

_____

THE POWER TO DREAM AGAIN!

POWER **TO** **DREAM**

"Unlocking The Mysteries of Dreams & Visions!"

_____

Date: _____ Time: _____

Scriptures: _____

_____

_____

_____

Significant Signs/Symbols:

_____

_____

_____

_____

_____

My Dream Was About:

_____

_____

_____

_____

_____

_____

_____

_____

_____

THE POWER TO DREAM AGAIN!

"Unlocking The Mysteries of Dreams & Visions!"

_____

_____

_____

_____

_____

_____

_____

_____

_____

_____

_____

_____

_____

_____

_____

_____

_____

_____

_____

_____

_____

_____

_____

_____

_____

_____

I will bless the Lord, who hath given me counsel: my reins also
instruct me in the night seasons. **Psalm 16:7**

"Unlocking The Mysteries of Dreams & Visions!"

"Unlocking The Mysteries of Dreams & Visions!"

_____

_____

_____

_____

_____

_____

_____

_____

_____

_____

_____

_____

_____

_____

_____

_____

_____

_____

_____

_____

_____

_____

_____

_____

_____

"Unlocking The Mysteries of Dreams & Visions!"

_____

_____

_____

_____

_____

_____

_____

_____

CONCLUSION: In addition to praying, what action needs to be taken or what change do you need to make?

_____

_____

_____

_____

_____

_____

_____

_____

_____

_____

_____

THE POWER TO DREAM AGAIN!

"Unlocking The Mysteries of Dreams & Visions!"

_____

Date: _____ Time: _____

Scriptures: _____

_____

_____

_____

Significant Signs/Symbols:

_____

_____

_____

_____

_____

My Dream Was About:

_____

_____

_____

_____

_____

_____

_____

_____

_____

THE POWER TO DREAM AGAIN!

"Unlocking The Mysteries of Dreams & Visions!"

_____

_____

_____

_____

_____

_____

_____

_____

_____

_____

_____

_____

_____

_____

_____

_____

_____

_____

_____

_____

_____

_____

_____

_____

_____

After these things the word of the Lord came unto Abram in a
vision, saying, Fear not, Abram: I am thy shield, and thy exceeding
great reward. **Genesis 15:1**

"Unlocking The Mysteries of Dreams & Visions!"

_____

_____

_____

_____

_____

_____

_____

_____

_____

_____

_____

_____

_____

_____

_____

_____

_____

_____

_____

_____

_____

_____

_____

_____

"Unlocking The Mysteries of Dreams & Visions!"

_____

_____

_____

_____

_____

_____

_____

_____

_____

_____

_____

_____

_____

_____

_____

_____

_____

_____

_____

_____

_____

_____

_____

_____

_____

_____

"Unlocking The Mysteries of Dreams & Visions!"

_____

_____

_____

_____

_____

_____

_____

_____

CONCLUSION: In addition to praying, what action needs to be taken or what change do you need to make?

_____

_____

_____

_____

_____

_____

_____

_____

_____

_____

THE POWER TO DREAM AGAIN!

POWER TO DREAM

"Unlocking The Mysteries of Dreams & Visions!"

_____

Date: _____ **Time:** _____

Scriptures: _____

_____

_____

_____

Significant Signs/Symbols:

_____

_____

_____

_____

_____

My Dream Was About:

_____

_____

_____

_____

_____

_____

_____

_____

_____

THE POWER TO DREAM AGAIN!

"Unlocking The Mysteries of Dreams & Visions!"

_____

_____

_____

_____

_____

_____

_____

_____

_____

_____

_____

_____

_____

_____

_____

_____

_____

_____

_____

_____

_____

_____

_____

But there is a God in heaven that revealeth secrets, and maketh
known to the king Nebuchadnezzar what shall be in the latter days.
Thy dream, and the visions of thy head upon thy bed, are these;
Daniel 2:28

"Unlocking The Mysteries of Dreams & Visions!"

_____

_____

_____

_____

_____

_____

_____

_____

_____

_____

_____

_____

_____

_____

_____

_____

_____

_____

_____

_____

_____

_____

_____

_____

_____

_____

_____

_____

"Unlocking The Mysteries of Dreams & Visions!"

_____

_____

_____

_____

_____

_____

_____

_____

_____

_____

_____

_____

_____

_____

_____

_____

_____

_____

_____

_____

_____

_____

_____

_____

_____

_____

_____

"Unlocking The Mysteries of Dreams & Visions!"

_____

_____

_____

_____

_____

_____

_____

_____

_____

_____

_____

_____

_____

_____

_____

_____

_____

_____

_____

_____

_____

_____

_____

_____

_____

_____

_____

_____

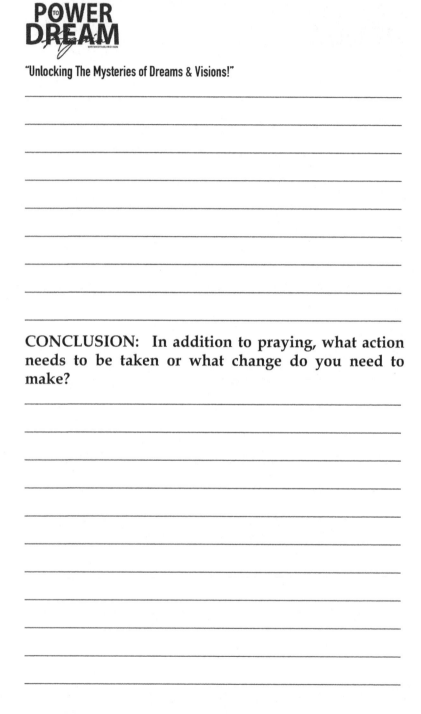

_____

_____

_____

_____

_____

_____

_____

_____

CONCLUSION: In addition to praying, what action needs to be taken or what change do you need to make?

_____

_____

_____

_____

_____

_____

_____

_____

_____

_____

_____

THE POWER TO DREAM AGAIN!

POWER to DREAM

"Unlocking The Mysteries of Dreams & Visions!"

Date: _____ Time: _____

Scriptures: _____

_____

_____

_____

Significant Signs/Symbols:

_____

_____

_____

_____

_____

My Dream Was About:

_____

_____

_____

_____

_____

_____

_____

_____

_____

THE POWER TO DREAM AGAIN!

"Unlocking The Mysteries of Dreams & Visions!"

_____

_____

_____

_____

_____

_____

_____

_____

_____

_____

_____

_____

_____

_____

_____

_____

_____

_____

_____

_____

_____

_____

_____

_____

_____

_____

And they said unto him, We have dreamed a dream, and there is
no interpreter of it. And Joseph said unto them, Do not
interpretations belong to God? tell me them, I pray you.
Genesis 40:8

"Unlocking The Mysteries of Dreams & Visions!"

"Unlocking The Mysteries of Dreams & Visions!"

_____

_____

_____

_____

_____

_____

_____

_____

_____

_____

_____

_____

_____

_____

_____

_____

_____

_____

_____

_____

_____

_____

_____

_____

_____

_____

"Unlocking The Mysteries of Dreams & Visions!"

_____

_____

_____

_____

_____

_____

_____

_____

_____

_____

_____

_____

_____

_____

_____

_____

_____

_____

_____

_____

_____

_____

_____

_____

_____

_____

_____

_____

_____

_____

_____

_____

_____

_____

_____

_____

_____

_____

CONCLUSION: In addition to praying, what action needs to be taken or what change do you need to make?

_____

_____

_____

_____

_____

_____

_____

_____

_____

_____

_____

_____

_____

THE POWER TO DREAM AGAIN!

"Unlocking The Mysteries of Dreams & Visions!"

_____

Date: _____ Time: _____

Scriptures: _____

_____

_____

_____

Significant Signs/Symbols:

_____

_____

_____

_____

_____

My Dream Was About:

_____

_____

_____

_____

_____

_____

_____

_____

_____

THE POWER TO DREAM AGAIN!

"Unlocking The Mysteries of Dreams & Visions!"

_____

_____

_____

_____

_____

_____

_____

_____

_____

_____

_____

_____

_____

_____

_____

_____

_____

_____

_____

_____

_____

_____

_____

Then thou spakest in vision to thy holy one, and saidst, I have laid help
upon one that is mighty; I have exalted one chosen out of the people.
Psalm 89:19

"Unlocking The Mysteries of Dreams & Visions!"

"Unlocking The Mysteries of Dreams & Visions!"

_____

_____

_____

_____

_____

_____

_____

_____

_____

_____

_____

_____

_____

_____

_____

_____

_____

_____

_____

_____

_____

_____

_____

_____

_____

_____

_____

_____

_____

"Unlocking The Mysteries of Dreams & Visions!"

_____

_____

_____

_____

_____

_____

_____

_____

_____

_____

_____

_____

_____

_____

_____

_____

_____

_____

_____

_____

_____

_____

_____

_____

_____

_____

_____

_____

_____

_____

_____

_____

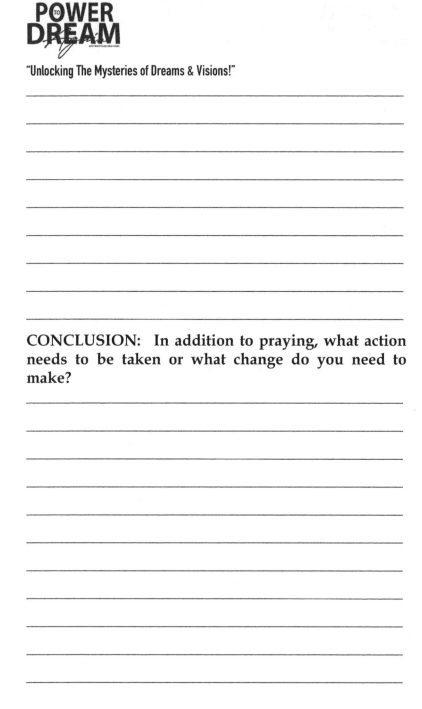

POWER DREAM

"Unlocking The Mysteries of Dreams & Visions!"

_____

_____

_____

_____

_____

_____

_____

_____

CONCLUSION: In addition to praying, what action needs to be taken or what change do you need to make?

_____

_____

_____

_____

_____

_____

_____

_____

_____

_____

_____

THE POWER TO DREAM AGAIN!

POWER TO DREAM

"Unlocking The Mysteries of Dreams & Visions!"

_____

Date: _____ Time: _____

Scriptures: _____

_____

_____

_____

Significant Signs/Symbols:

_____

_____

_____

_____

_____

My Dream Was About:

_____

_____

_____

_____

_____

_____

_____

_____

_____

THE POWER TO DREAM AGAIN!

"Unlocking The Mysteries of Dreams & Visions!"

_____

_____

_____

_____

_____

_____

_____

_____

_____

_____

_____

_____

_____

_____

_____

_____

_____

_____

_____

_____

_____

_____

_____

_____

_____

The hand of the Lord was upon me, and carried me out in the
spirit of the Lord, and set me down in the midst of the valley which
was full of bones, **Ezekiel 37:1**

"Unlocking The Mysteries of Dreams & Visions!"

_____

_____

_____

_____

_____

_____

_____

_____

_____

_____

_____

_____

_____

_____

_____

_____

_____

_____

_____

_____

_____

"Unlocking The Mysteries of Dreams & Visions!"

"Unlocking The Mysteries of Dreams & Visions!"

_____

_____

_____

_____

_____

_____

_____

_____

_____

_____

_____

_____

_____

_____

_____

_____

_____

_____

_____

_____

_____

_____

_____

_____

_____

_____

_____

_____

_____

_____

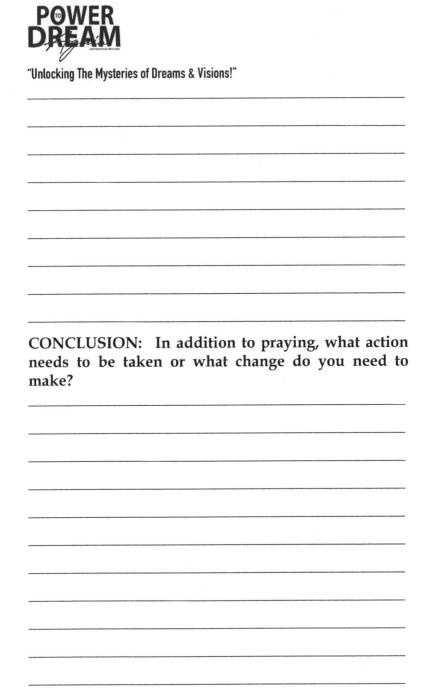

_____

_____

_____

_____

_____

_____

_____

_____

CONCLUSION: In addition to praying, what action needs to be taken or what change do you need to make?

_____

_____

_____

_____

_____

_____

_____

_____

_____

_____

THE POWER TO DREAM AGAIN!

POWER TO DREAM

"Unlocking The Mysteries of Dreams & Visions!"

Date: _____ Time: _____

Scriptures: _____

_____

_____

_____

Significant Signs/Symbols:

_____

_____

_____

_____

_____

My Dream Was About:

_____

_____

_____

_____

_____

_____

_____

_____

_____

_____

THE POWER TO DREAM AGAIN!

POWER DREAM

"Unlocking The Mysteries of Dreams & Visions!"

_____

_____

_____

_____

_____

_____

_____

_____

_____

_____

_____

_____

_____

_____

_____

_____

_____

_____

_____

_____

_____

_____

_____

And I knew such a man, (whether in the body, or out of the body, I
cannot tell: God knoweth;) **2 Corinthians 12:3**

"Unlocking The Mysteries of Dreams & Visions!"

_____

_____

_____

_____

_____

_____

_____

_____

_____

_____

_____

_____

_____

_____

_____

_____

_____

_____

_____

_____

_____

_____

_____

"Unlocking The Mysteries of Dreams & Visions!"

"Unlocking The Mysteries of Dreams & Visions!"

_____

_____

_____

_____

_____

_____

_____

_____

_____

_____

_____

_____

_____

_____

_____

_____

_____

_____

_____

_____

_____

_____

_____

_____

_____

_____

_____

_____

_____

_____

_____

_____

_____

_____

_____

_____

_____

_____

_____

CONCLUSION: In addition to praying, what action needs to be taken or what change do you need to make?

_____

_____

_____

_____

_____

_____

_____

_____

_____

_____

_____

THE POWER TO DREAM AGAIN!

"Unlocking The Mysteries of Dreams & Visions!"

Date: _____ Time: _____

Scriptures: _____

_____

_____

_____

Significant Signs/Symbols:

_____

_____

_____

_____

_____

My Dream Was About:

_____

_____

_____

_____

_____

_____

_____

_____

_____

THE POWER TO DREAM AGAIN!

"Unlocking The Mysteries of Dreams & Visions!"

_____

_____

_____

_____

_____

_____

_____

_____

_____

_____

_____

_____

_____

_____

_____

_____

_____

_____

_____

_____

_____

_____

_____

_____

_____

_____

_____

And he said, Unto you it is given to know the mysteries of the kingdom of God: but to others in parables; **Luke 8:10**

"Unlocking The Mysteries of Dreams & Visions!"

POWER to DREAM

"Unlocking The Mysteries of Dreams & Visions!"

"Unlocking The Mysteries of Dreams & Visions!"

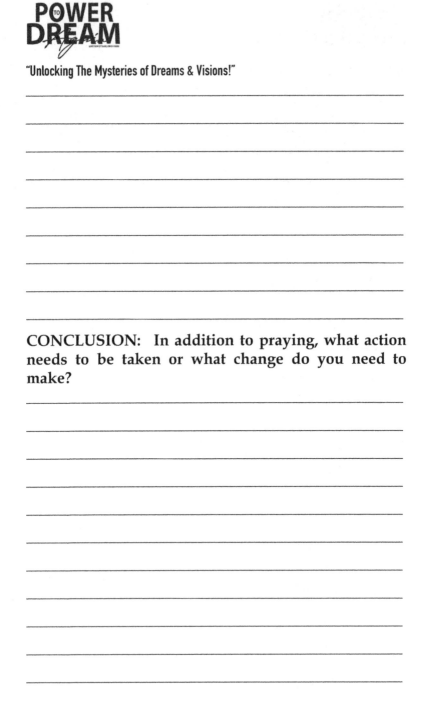

_____

_____

_____

_____

_____

_____

_____

_____

_____

CONCLUSION: In addition to praying, what action needs to be taken or what change do you need to make?

_____

_____

_____

_____

_____

_____

_____

_____

_____

_____

_____

THE POWER TO DREAM AGAIN!

Date: _____ Time: _____

Scriptures: _____

_____

_____

_____

Significant Signs/Symbols:

_____

_____

_____

_____

_____

My Dream Was About:

_____

_____

_____

_____

_____

_____

_____

_____

_____

THE POWER TO DREAM AGAIN!

"Unlocking The Mysteries of Dreams & Visions!"

_____

_____

_____

_____

_____

_____

_____

_____

_____

_____

_____

_____

_____

_____

_____

_____

_____

_____

_____

_____

_____

_____

_____

_____

_____

Then was the secret revealed unto Daniel in a night vision.
Then Daniel blessed the God of heaven.
Daniel 2:19

"Unlocking The Mysteries of Dreams & Visions!"

_____

_____

_____

_____

_____

_____

_____

_____

_____

_____

_____

_____

_____

_____

_____

_____

_____

_____

_____

_____

_____

_____

_____

_____

_____

_____

_____

_____

"Unlocking The Mysteries of Dreams & Visions!"

_____
_____
_____
_____
_____
_____
_____
_____
_____
_____
_____
_____
_____
_____
_____
_____
_____
_____
_____
_____
_____
_____
_____
_____

"Unlocking The Mysteries of Dreams & Visions!"

_____

_____

_____

_____

_____

_____

_____

_____

_____

_____

_____

_____

_____

_____

_____

_____

_____

_____

_____

_____

_____

_____

_____

_____

_____

_____

_____

_____

_____

_____

_____

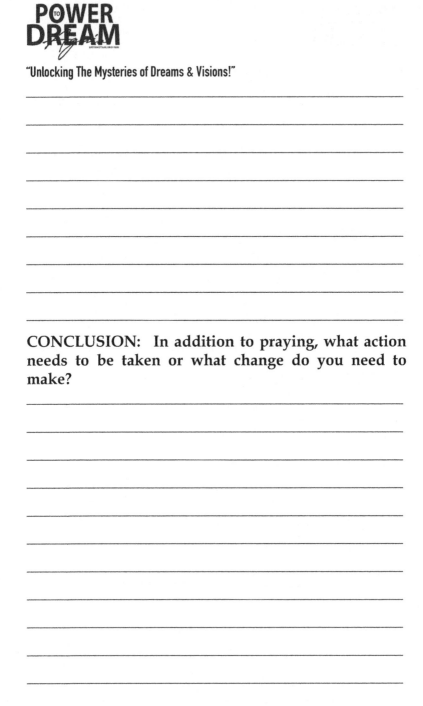

POWER to DREAM

"Unlocking The Mysteries of Dreams & Visions!"

_____

_____

_____

_____

_____

_____

_____

_____

CONCLUSION: In addition to praying, what action needs to be taken or what change do you need to make?

_____

_____

_____

_____

_____

_____

_____

_____

_____

_____

THE POWER TO DREAM AGAIN!

"Unlocking The Mysteries of Dreams & Visions!"

_____

Date: _____ Time: _____

Scriptures: _____

_____

_____

_____

Significant Signs/Symbols:

_____

_____

_____

_____

_____

My Dream Was About:

_____

_____

_____

_____

_____

_____

_____

_____

_____

THE POWER TO DREAM AGAIN!

"Unlocking The Mysteries of Dreams & Visions!"

_____

_____

_____

_____

_____

_____

_____

_____

_____

_____

_____

_____

_____

_____

_____

_____

_____

_____

_____

_____

_____

_____

_____

_____

_____

_____

But God came to Abimelech in a dream by night, and said to him,
Behold, thou art but a dead man, for the woman which thou hast taken;
for she is a man's wife. **Genesis 20:3**

"Unlocking The Mysteries of Dreams & Visions!"

_____

_____

_____

_____

_____

_____

_____

_____

_____

_____

_____

_____

_____

_____

_____

_____

_____

_____

_____

_____

_____

_____

_____

_____

_____

_____

_____

_____

"Unlocking The Mysteries of Dreams & Visions!"

_____

_____

_____

_____

_____

_____

_____

_____

_____

_____

_____

_____

_____

_____

_____

_____

_____

_____

_____

_____

_____

_____

_____

"Unlocking The Mysteries of Dreams & Visions!"

_____

_____

_____

_____

_____

_____

_____

_____

_____

_____

_____

_____

_____

_____

_____

_____

_____

_____

_____

_____

_____

_____

_____

_____

_____

_____

_____

_____

_____

_____

_____

_____

_____

_____

_____

_____

_____

_____

CONCLUSION: In addition to praying, what action needs to be taken or what change do you need to make?

_____

_____

_____

_____

_____

_____

_____

_____

_____

_____

_____

THE POWER TO DREAM AGAIN!

"Unlocking The Mysteries of Dreams & Visions!"

_____

Date: _____ Time: _____

Scriptures: _____

_____

_____

_____

Significant Signs/Symbols:

_____

_____

_____

_____

_____

My Dream Was About:

_____

_____

_____

_____

_____

_____

_____

_____

_____

THE POWER TO DREAM AGAIN!

"Unlocking The Mysteries of Dreams & Visions!"

_____

_____

_____

_____

_____

_____

_____

_____

_____

_____

_____

_____

_____

_____

_____

_____

_____

_____

_____

_____

_____

_____

_____

_____

God also bearing them witness, both with signs and wonders, and with divers miracles, and gifts of the Holy Ghost, according to his own will?
Hebrews 2:4

"Unlocking The Mysteries of Dreams & Visions!"

_____

_____

_____

_____

_____

_____

_____

_____

_____

_____

_____

_____

_____

_____

_____

_____

_____

_____

_____

_____

_____

_____

_____

_____

_____

_____

_____

_____

_____

"Unlocking The Mysteries of Dreams & Visions!"

_____

_____

_____

_____

_____

_____

_____

_____

_____

_____

_____

_____

_____

_____

_____

_____

_____

_____

_____

_____

_____

_____

_____

_____

_____

_____

_____

"Unlocking The Mysteries of Dreams & Visions!"

_____

_____

_____

_____

_____

_____

_____

_____

_____

_____

_____

_____

_____

_____

_____

_____

_____

_____

_____

_____

_____

_____

_____

_____

_____

_____

_____

_____

_____

_____

_____

_____

_____

_____

_____

_____

CONCLUSION: In addition to praying, what action needs to be taken or what change do you need to make?

_____

_____

_____

_____

_____

_____

_____

_____

_____

_____

_____

THE POWER TO DREAM AGAIN!

POWER TO DREAM

"Unlocking The Mysteries of Dreams & Visions!"

_____

Date: _____ Time: _____

Scriptures: _____

_____

_____

_____

Significant Signs/Symbols:

_____

_____

_____

_____

_____

My Dream Was About:

_____

_____

_____

_____

_____

_____

_____

_____

_____

THE POWER TO DREAM AGAIN!

"Unlocking The Mysteries of Dreams & Visions!"

And this shall be a sign unto thee from the Lord, that the Lord will do this thing that he hath spoken; **Isaiah 38:7**

"Unlocking The Mysteries of Dreams & Visions!"

"Unlocking The Mysteries of Dreams & Visions!"

_____

_____

_____

_____

_____

_____

_____

_____

_____

_____

_____

_____

_____

_____

_____

_____

_____

_____

_____

_____

_____

_____

_____

_____

_____

_____

"Unlocking The Mysteries of Dreams & Visions!"

_____

_____

_____

_____

_____

_____

_____

_____

_____

_____

_____

_____

_____

_____

_____

_____

_____

_____

_____

_____

_____

_____

_____

_____

_____

_____

_____

_____

_____

_____

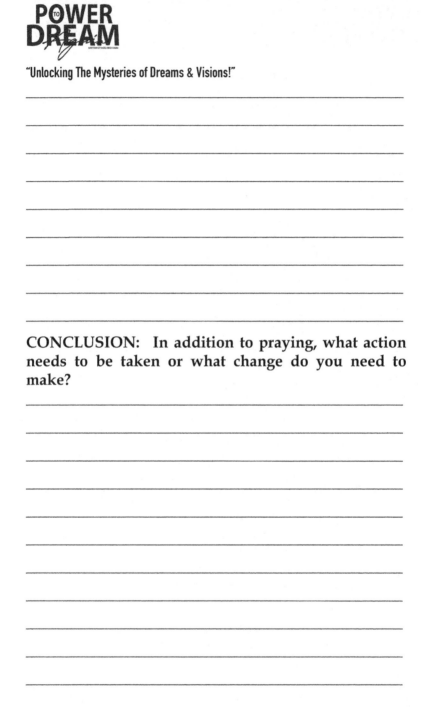

POWER TO DREAM

"Unlocking The Mysteries of Dreams & Visions!"

_____

_____

_____

_____

_____

_____

_____

_____

CONCLUSION: In addition to praying, what action needs to be taken or what change do you need to make?

_____

_____

_____

_____

_____

_____

_____

_____

_____

_____

_____

THE POWER TO DREAM AGAIN!

POWER TO DREAM

"Unlocking The Mysteries of Dreams & Visions!"

Date: _____ Time: _____

Scriptures: _____
_____
_____
_____

Significant Signs/Symbols:

_____
_____
_____
_____
_____

My Dream Was About:

_____
_____
_____
_____
_____
_____
_____
_____
_____

THE POWER TO DREAM AGAIN!

"Unlocking The Mysteries of Dreams & Visions!"

_____
_____
_____
_____
_____
_____
_____
_____
_____
_____
_____
_____
_____
_____
_____
_____
_____
_____
_____
_____
_____
_____
_____
_____
_____
_____
_____
_____
_____
_____

In my Father's house are many mansions: if it were not so, I would
have told you. I go to prepare a place for you. **John 14:2**

"Unlocking The Mysteries of Dreams & Visions!"

_____

_____

_____

_____

_____

_____

_____

_____

_____

_____

_____

_____

_____

_____

_____

_____

_____

_____

_____

_____

_____

_____

_____

_____

_____

_____

_____

_____

_____

"Unlocking The Mysteries of Dreams & Visions!"

_____

_____

_____

_____

_____

_____

_____

_____

_____

_____

_____

_____

_____

_____

_____

_____

_____

_____

_____

_____

_____

_____

_____

_____

_____

_____

_____

"Unlocking The Mysteries of Dreams & Visions!"

POWER TO DREAM

"Unlocking The Mysteries of Dreams & Visions!"

_____

_____

_____

_____

_____

_____

_____

_____

CONCLUSION: In addition to praying, what action needs to be taken or what change do you need to make?

_____

_____

_____

_____

_____

_____

_____

_____

_____

_____

_____

THE POWER TO DREAM AGAIN!

"Unlocking The Mysteries of Dreams & Visions!"

_____

Date: _____ Time: _____

Scriptures: _____

           _____

           _____

           _____

Significant Signs/Symbols:

           _____

           _____

           _____

           _____

           _____

My Dream Was About:

_____

_____

_____

_____

_____

_____

_____

_____

_____

THE POWER TO DREAM AGAIN!

"Unlocking The Mysteries of Dreams & Visions!"

_____

_____

_____

_____

_____

_____

_____

_____

_____

_____

_____

_____

_____

_____

_____

_____

_____

_____

_____

_____

_____

_____

_____

_____

_____

14 For God speaketh once, yea twice, yet man perceiveth it not.
15 In a dream, in a vision of the night, when deep sleep falleth upon men,
in slumberings upon the bed; **Job 33:14, 15**

"Unlocking The Mysteries of Dreams & Visions!"

_____

_____

_____

_____

_____

_____

_____

_____

_____

_____

_____

_____

_____

_____

_____

_____

_____

_____

_____

_____

_____

_____

_____

_____

_____

_____

_____

_____

_____

"Unlocking The Mysteries of Dreams & Visions!"

"Unlocking The Mysteries of Dreams & Visions!"

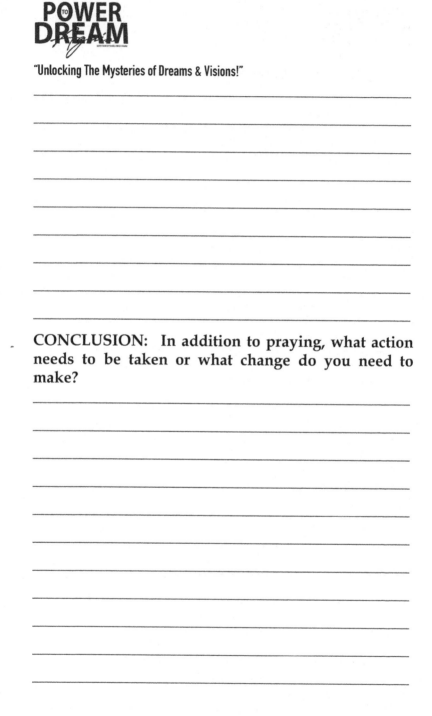

POWER TO DREAM

"Unlocking The Mysteries of Dreams & Visions!"

_____

_____

_____

_____

_____

_____

_____

_____

CONCLUSION: In addition to praying, what action needs to be taken or what change do you need to make?

_____

_____

_____

_____

_____

_____

_____

_____

_____

_____

THE POWER TO DREAM AGAIN!

"Unlocking The Mysteries of Dreams & Visions!"

Thank you for embracing the power to dream again....your journey has just begun!

Whatsoever things are true, whatsoever things are honest, whatsoever things are just, whatsoever things are pure, whatsoever things are lovely, whatsoever things are of good report; if there be any virtue and if there be any praise, think on these things
Philippians 4:8

POWER TO DREAM AGAIN

"Unlocking the Mysteries of Dreams and Visions"

Made in the USA
Coppell, TX
05 February 2022

72936823R00115